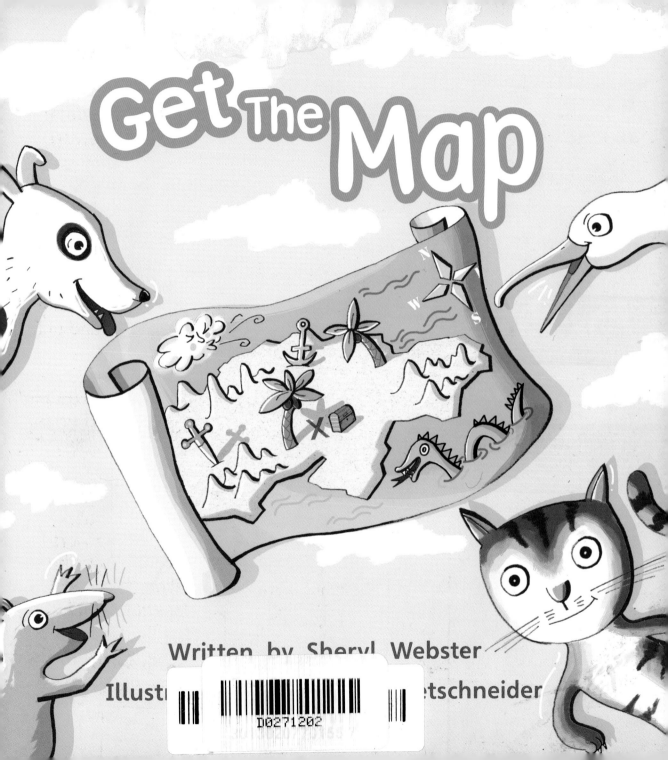

Get The Map

Written by Sheryl Webster

Illust... ...etschneider

Gull can nip off to get the map.

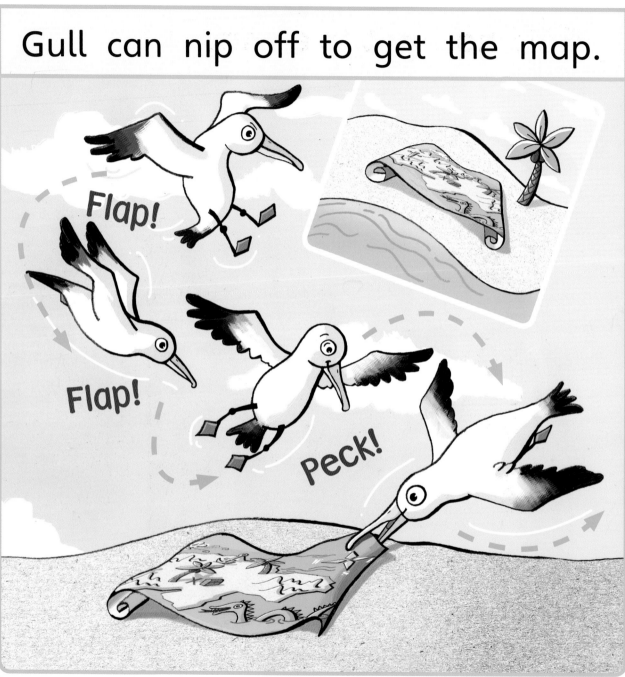

Gull has got the map.

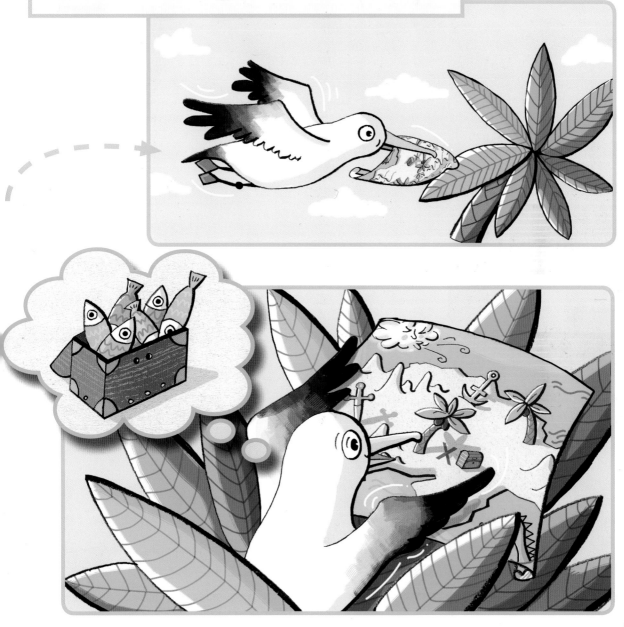

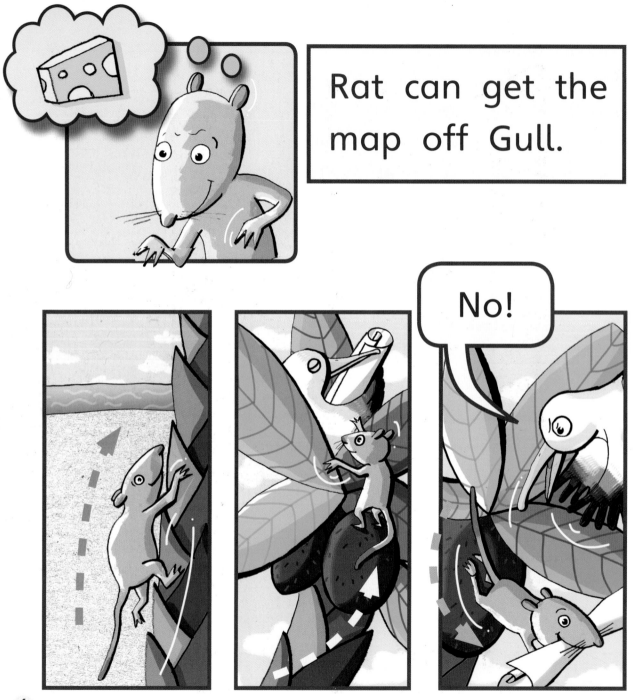

Rat can get the map off Gull.

No!

4

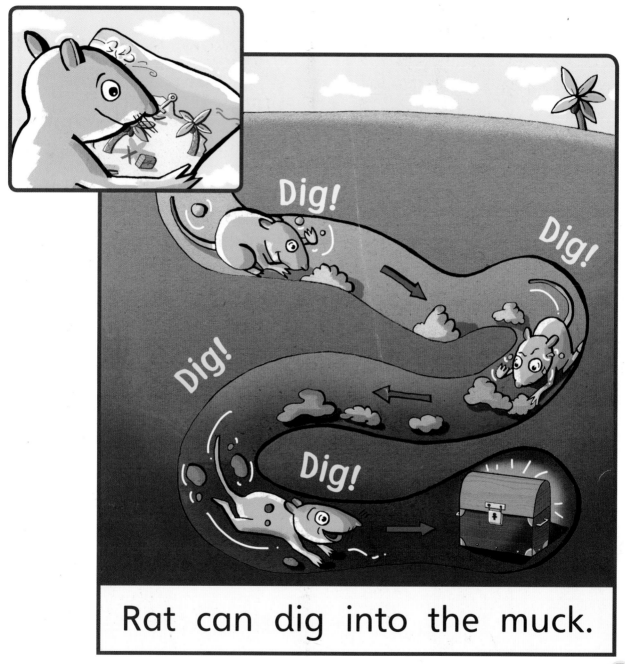

Rat can dig into the muck.

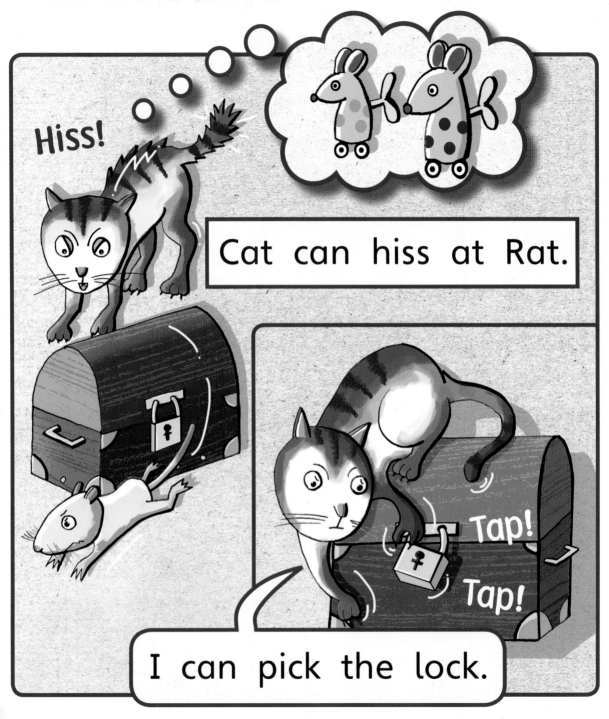

Dog can run at Cat.

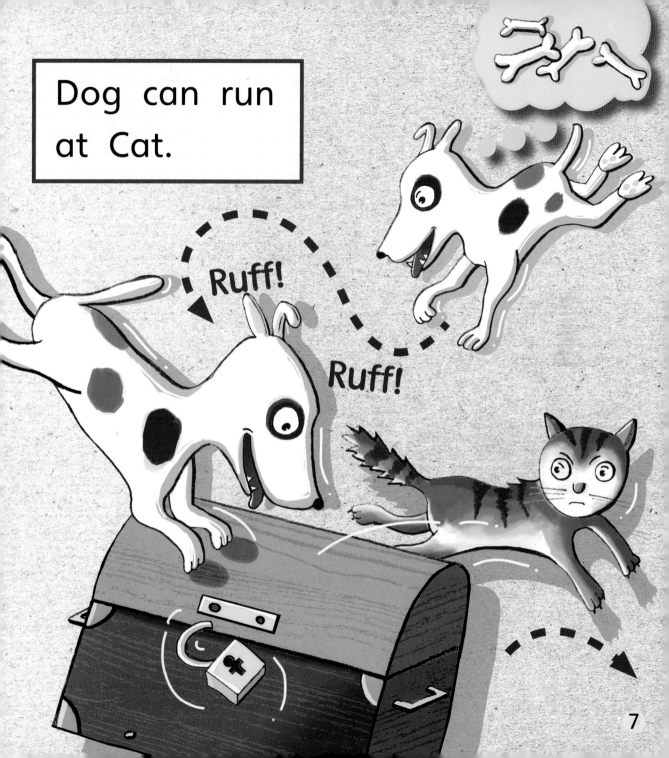

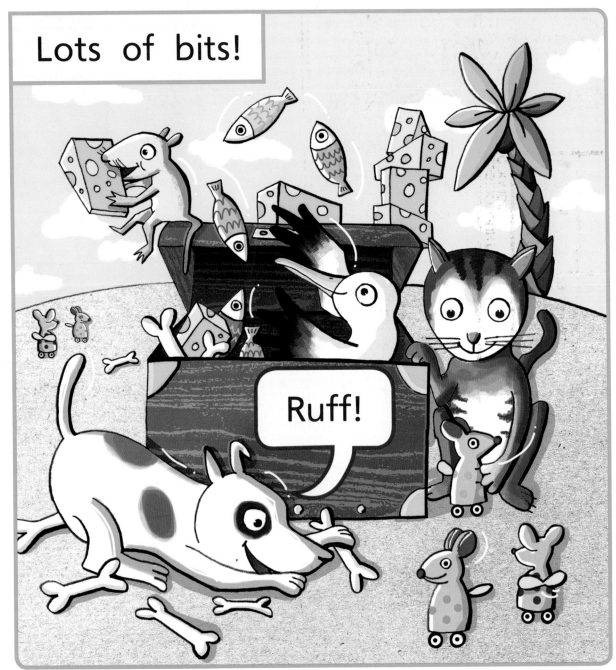